HER

Peace

OF

MIND

LIZ FRISBY

Cover designed by Sean M. Lassiter
Editing by Chana Twiggs
Manufactured in the United States of America

Special Thanks to Marcus Godfrey, Rodney Jean Jacques, Candace M.
Braddock, Kimberly Jennings, LaToya Stephens, John Stephens, Ebonie
Dukes, Regina Meacham-Devero & all family & friends who've expressed
support.

For Mom

_____ξ_____

The Queen of my heart
May you continue to rest in eternal peace

For Sean Sr. & Sean Jr.

_____ξ_____

You, both, are my living illustrations of love

CONTENTS

§

INTRODUCTION

§

"I am ready for love, why are you hiding from me? I'd simply give my freedom to be held in your captivity." Oh India Arie sings these lyrics so well that I can feel each word tug at my heart and has me almost moved to tears. Pick me! Choose me! Marry me! Anybody! Somebody! Please! The life of a single woman in this day and age is downright depressing. To suffer heartache after heartache, disappointment after disappointment; a woman is bound to become an emotional insecure wreck. Just think about the following scenario.

You see him. He sees you & notices you noticing him. You both look away and then glance back as soon as you think the other isn't paying attention. You attempt to get a better look at this man. "Am I really attracted to him", you ask yourself. You have to make certain it isn't a fluke and he really is *fine*. Yes, he is yummy! Okay, now that's out of the way it's time to do some inventory. Nice smile? Check! Well dressed? Check! Are other women admiring this tasty piece of flesh? Check! Oh yes, he just may be worth a bit more attention. Let the flirting begin! The encounter becomes a success and ends with phone numbers being exchanged. Yay!

A few telephone conversations ensue then dinner & a movie, maybe bowling or a walk in the park. You notice how excited you get when he calls; you get *butterflies* – oh the feeling has never been so enjoyable. Being the hopeful romantic and optimistic woman that you are, you imagine a life with this man. You envision a future; meeting his mother, hoping his sisters like you, what would the kids look like? Hoping they'd inherit his eyes because you drown in them every time he looks at you. Yeah – you're *in love*. It's official – you're floating on cloud nine. Lucky you!

Then, without warning, *something* happens. You don't know why but all of a sudden those fluffy white clouds that carried you effortlessly have now disappeared. Reality sinks in and you fall out of the light blue sky and SMACK face down on the concrete. OUCH! People are watching; waiting for your next move but no one bothers to extend a hand and help you get up. You're too embarrassed to even look up so you just lay there hoping that you become unconscious from the impact of the fall. Praying that when you awake it was all a dream and you're still *in love*. Sorry honey, but it was all real and so is the pain that rest on your chest like a shipload of bricks.

So here you are all alone with your thoughts of single life (dreading being alone forever) and they go something like this:

I am standing alone on ground that has existed longer than I
have lived
A world whose history encompasses endless accounts of life
forgotten
Untold stories of days long lived but forever lost because no
one was there to witness
Their open palms were left bare with only their own skin to
caress

Their lonesome arms dangled at their sides aching for flesh to
embrace
Their eyes blurred with desperate tears relentlessly searching
for a welcoming face
For someone – anyone who would attempt to care
Offering their most valuable possession – their time, just to be
there
Sadly, no one took the time to even smile in their direction
They were born, they lived and they died; their life a complete
rejection
Discarded by those that walked this very ground on which I
now stand
Alone and neglected – waiting for someone – anyone, to hold
my hand
...Forgotten!

My own relationship experiences have left me questioning who I am and here's what I've come up with: I am a pair of breasts, pale legs, a vagina and a little booty, but I assure you there's so much more to me. If one would take the time to see past the physique they would discover there is a captive soul yearning (like an innocent prisoner of war held captive since birth – *yearning*) to be set free. If they were to pause for a moment and actually get to know me they would learn of decades of self-inflicted repression. I have spent years of my life enslaved to misconceptions pertaining to ideologies of love (for self and for others) and womanhood. Though I am very certain that the two are positively correlated, I ignorantly yet confidently believed that I understood each as undoubtedly as I did the alphabet. My lifestyle, relationships and decisions were based around my understanding of love. As long as I gave it (to whomever) I would receive it in return, and if I loved myself then others would love me as well. What exactly was I giving though? How do you *give* love? What is love? Notice my theory doesn't include a clear definition of love itself – I just knew it existed and I possessed the innate ability to love, *somehow*. It was just that simple. And since I was born female it was obvious that I encompassed and knew everything there was to know about being a woman.

Unfortunately, I have learned that all of the above is BULL CRAP! It has to be; otherwise I wouldn't experience disappointment after disappointments and heartache after heartaches. If my theory were accurate I'd be married by now. Clearly I am missing something here. For example, a sign that reads:

**"LOVE TAKES A LIFETIME TO UNDERSTAND
& YOU RUN THE RISK OF LOSING YOUR
MIND IN THE PROCESS!**

**P.S. YOU OBVIOUSLY KNOW NOTHING
ABOUT BEING A *WOMAN*"**

However, there is hope…

A woman is born

Distinguished from others by far more than just her name
Her life, predestined
Meticulously formed
From the shade of her skin to the blood in her veins
She gasps, taking in her first breath
She lives, born into royalty
Instantly bestowed upon as a Queen
Along the way
Peasants will try to confine her mind
But her King will free her just in time.

Daydreaming

§

Ever since my excursion through the birth canal I have been molded via my environment, society and the media into a "woman" and Lord knows that being a woman is complicated. Of course there are the monthly emotional breakdowns when it seems as if no one else in the world could comprehend how I am feeling, known to some as "the curse". That earth shattering week when everything seems to be a catastrophe; I hate my job, I wonder why I even went to college and spent so much damn money to obtain a piece of freakin' paper, I feel fat and I can't fit my good jeans, my mood is as unpredictable as the future. I sit on the sofa and sob because I have no clue as to what else to do. I reevaluate my existence – why am I even here? The world would be better off without me! *I* don't even want to be bothered with *me*! So, I spontaneously and erratically decide, "yes, I should just end it all right here and right now." Subsequently I realize suicide would be too painful and I don't have the guts to attempt ending my own life in fear of surviving and having to live with the embarrassment and/or any health repercussions I may have caused myself. Fortunately, times such as these only occur once a month and for approximately four decades of a woman's life – I pray I can cope with these (hopefully accurate) estimates.

Then, to make the role of my gender even more technical there's the agonizing decision of what shade of lipstick matches my attire. You can pretend if you want but keeping up to date with the fashion world is a struggle for me. Considering that trends seem to change with every season and somehow still manage to revert back to styles from previous decades, I am confused as to whether or not I should attempt to match or just throw color schemes together and hope for the best. Am I wrong if my belt coordinates with my shoes and purse? Would I be considered fashionably illiterate if I don't understand Ugg boots with short mini shirts? I have been so puzzled at times that the thought of prancing around naked actually seemed appealing. Then reality struck and that idea was thrown out of the window when even I shunned away from reflections of my back fat, kangaroo pouch and love handles in my long, truth-revealing mirror. I digress.

Now, onto a more important matter, all women have insecurities that if we have to we will run around wearing army fatigues to conceal. If I want to survive in this ever changing and rapidly forming insensitive and hard knock culture, I must portray that I am as confident as Alicia Keys on stage performing "Superwoman" as the lyrics declare "…even when I'm a mess I still put on a vest with an "S" on my chest, oh yes I'm a superwoman." I dare not reveal my weaknesses or fears; besides I don't have the time with the many roles that I have been cultured to play.

As a woman, I have learned to try my best to be a nurturing caregiver. To cater to my family and friends; those I hold close to my heart. To make sure they have the necessities in life, to comfort and soothe them when necessary and to always – ALWAYS be there when they need me. I can do it! I am strong and I know that God never puts more on me then I can bear so hey, my shoulders may be small, but they must be sturdy enough to carry the load. If men could do it alone then poor Adam would've never had his rib taken from him in the middle of his nap. So therefore, I have to step up; I have to acknowledge God's decision for the existence of my gender. I was chosen to be a woman and I must accept and embrace my obligation to womanhood. I am woman...hear me roar! Notice how I take on the world despite my own feelings of inadequacy. The lion may be the king of the jungle but the lioness is the necessary predator that feeds the entire pride. I am a *Superwoman* and there is nothing I cannot handle on my own. Right? One would surely hope so. Sorrowfully, if the truth were to be told, despite my self-defined womanly agenda, even with my attempt to portray that I have it all together, acknowledging that I am human and not a beast of the jungle (except in the bedroom), ignoring the societal order of things and admitting my own needs, I AM LONELY.

Yeah, I said it! I embarrassingly admit that I am lonely! I am desperately (and I mean *desperately* – like a starving child that you see on one of those fundraising commercials; all frail and skinny, whose life could be forever changed for the better with just one bowl of rice – *desperately*) in pursuit of companionship. However, I am not seeking just any companionship. I could easily *settle* down with someone who would worship the infectious, mucus-infiltrated saliva that I'd spit into a toilet bowl while attempting to rid my body of pneumonia, and know that he really does love *me* and I not love him in return. That would be settling. One of my biggest fears as a woman is that my short lived and precious time on earth could possibly be consumed with well hidden misery while enduring a relationship (or marriage even) with a man that loves me with his whole entire being, and that he could still not be good enough. Nonetheless, he'd be living and moving flesh with a heart and a brain so he could very well be sufficient companionship.

Considering that I walk under a large umbrella of emotionally unstable and time-consuming obligations as a woman, I need someone just to be there. It's as simple as that. I desire a man by my side to go along for the ride. I believe it is his responsibility to take care of me, to *love* (there goes that word again) me. He is supposed to be there to encourage me and give me that supportive nudge when I feel as if I've exerted all that I ever can. To warmly embrace me with a sweet and endearing kiss on the cheek or the back of my neck just to let me know that he is here for *me*. My "king of the jungle" would serve as the cure to my self-diagnosed and life-threatening disease called loneliness. I would no longer have the worry of who would be there to assure me that I am not traveling this road through life alone. Nowadays the divorce rate is so high that longevity of a marriage still isn't promised, but for now I'll keep an optimistic perspective. He would be my *"someone"* to share the wonderful, amazing, indescribable, mysteriously timed moments of life with, and a witness to my existence. His happiness would be a testament of my accomplishments as a woman; a compliment of who I am – "a *Superwoman*."

But regardless, I still cannot settle for *any* man. That just isn't good enough for me. I want my knight in shining armor, my prince to rescue this damsel in distress (before she pulls her hair out), my king and everything and anything less is unacceptable. So while I'm living out my normal routine trying to be every woman (at least the forty weeks out of the year when I am not suicidal) I still have to add to my multitasking duties and continuously pursue My Man.

The ultimate question is: how do I know what to look for? Is it physical attraction? Should I focus on whether or not he has a job with benefits? Should he have the same spiritual beliefs as I do? Is there such a things as chemistry? What about love at first sight? How will I know *who* he is? Will he touch my hand and instantly warmth consumes my earthly flesh, leaving me feeling high and believing that I am immortal? Will my eyes well up with tears at the sight of my divinely appointed (if there is even such a thing) sent from heaven king? Is it possible that I already know who he is? Have I known him my whole life and just not recognized him as "the one?" Have I dated him already? Does this man even exist?

I'm seeking so much more

Anticipating future events
Praying that tomorrow expedites what's next
I am impatient and I'm not ashamed
I boast of my anxiety
I am sick from living in "the same"

I'm seeking so much more

My lungs are polluted with recycled air
My mind is under stimulated
My heart is burdened because she dares

To desire for my legs to move on new land
For my fingers to caress a stranger's hands

I'm seeking so much more
To feel a new breeze against my skin
For diverse sceneries for my eyes to vision
I'm nauseous from the usual
I ache for the scent of fresh to tickle to my nose
The taste of authentic rather than manipulations of originals

I'm seeking so much more

A transformation of all I've known
To learn, to move, to fear and to grow
Out of my comfort zone
To feel uneasy because I'm unfamiliar
To become acquainted with that which is not similar

And love it because it is so much more!

Wait a minute…wait just one minute, who is Handsome over there?

Could he possibly have the potential?

Did he just look my direction?

Oh my Lord, did he just pay me some attention?

Paused –
For a moment the two were no longer in orbit
The crowded room instantly stood still and became silent
Those who were near seemed to be very distant
It was a bit puzzling but surely comfortable
As their eyes met and lingered for an inexpressible few seconds

Just a moment –
An instant where everything inside felt balanced
Pride and egos weren't interfering
It was as if their souls had emerged and were communicating
Though no one else could hear, they simply whispered
Admitting their attraction; acknowledging the evident appeal

Suddenly –
He blinked and in reaction she did too
Disappointingly brought back to the reality of a noisy and
crowded room
Both were too proud to try and capture the moment again
Too intimidated to give in and look in the other's direction
Feeling uneasy the two leave it at eye contact, fearful of
speaking.

I see you watching me

So I pinch my cheeks and lick my lips

Sway my hips with extra force

In an attempt to taunt your pleading eyes

As they glaringly beg to visualize more

My movements and mannerisms are seductively slow

A slight smile here

And an "oops I dropped something; could you get that for me?" there

I am your one-woman show

Oh my name?

Sure, it's whatever you'd like

Oh my aim?

Well I can only tell you but so much on the first night

But this I will share

I observed you observing me

And I must admit – I like it when you stare

So keep watching…

I dreamt of you
I saw your face
Flawless

I heard your voice
Confident and soothing

You were there
And I was sure

I promise to dream of you tonight
I'll meet you again

In that place
Where darkness overtakes the light

I only ask
That you dream of me also.

Daydreaming and I'm thinking of him, I don't understand it
My emotions are on a rampage
I'm incapable of providing an explanation
I've been swept off my feet and carried away to an internal
destination
All inclusive
With a wide variety of all I could consume
Everything tailored to my desires
From the star count in the night's sky to the luminosity of the
moon
An excursion of endless possibilities
Feeling adventurous, I close my eyes
Open my arms and allow the breeze to carry me
Lifting me effortlessly as I defy gravity
Gliding through certainty and security
Hovering over reality while enjoying thoughts of his affection
Oh what I'd give for the ability to know his intentions
Daydreaming and I'm thinking of him
I wonder what he's thinking
Could he too feel the breeze?
Or will my lonely sentiments linger in the air?
Waiting to occupy his mind; waiting for him to recognize that
they are there
Anticipating being his daydream.

Quietly
He walks across my heart
Barely leaving footprints
Just unidentifiable marks
He doesn't say much
And when he does it's just a whisper
At times I have to watch the movement of his lips
Just so I could decipher
What it is he wants to express
Wishing he'd say it louder
I'm not attracted to the shy type
Yet something keeps me around a bit longer
More than likely, it's curiosity
The challenge is always appealing
Still I have to be careful
It's the quiet ones who creep up on me.

Whisper to me
Quietly share
Your ambitions, your fears, your worries

Just whisper to me
And I promise to catch them in the air

All I need is a whisper
I've been listening for a while now
I'm able
I'm ready
I'm listening.

Ahhhh – the ignorance of a fresh discovery

The innocence

The ability to mentally design you to my liking

Ideal

You are complete and you could possibly complete me

Faultless

You could cause no damage – I am open

Vulnerable

I have confidence in you – it's your obligation to maintain

Smitten

I am purely infatuated – I cherish the grace period

Breathtaking

Ahhhh – the premature bliss.

I inhale you as if you're the last breath I'll ever take

Hesitant to exhale – I silently whistle, praying that all of your sweetness won't escape

I open my eyes – delightfully you're still in front of me.

Please don't be an illusion – my heart can't withstand the agony

I reach out to touch what I plead in my mind to be flesh

Pleasantly you reach back and together our hands gently rest

My pulse begins to race as my palms sweat and my eyes begin to chase

Every single part of you; your legs, your chest and satisfyingly – your face

There is a radiance surrounding you that I choose to see

It illuminates everything about you and pours out every time you speak

I am hanging on every word; each syllable, as if they would go extinct

Attempting to capture something so priceless, so rare – something so distinct

The sun has finally arrived; gently peaking through my heart

She brings the joy of the morning with sweet sorrow for we must now part

My life has forever changed; every breath now more meaningful

My spirit – which was once restrained – is now free, appreciative and hopeful.

A glimpse

A snapshot of utopia

Intriguing all senses, emotions and aspirations

Leaving me with just a taste of succulent samples

Previews of potential fulfillment

I'm more than interested

I'm almost ready to devour…

Or put more eloquently, "experience" your delightfulness

I'm sold.

I close my eyes purposely
Prepared to wander in the dark
Though I know I won't have to
For my heart will follow your heart

I won't ask any questions
Though many are evolving in my mind
I'll remain silent and just listen
Waiting for your heart to give my heart a sign

Yours beats rapidly
And in response my heart jumps too
I heard her silently whisper to him
Dear Heart, My Heart – I will trust you.

A feeling

A bit more than exhilarating

As if I'm seven years old on Christmas Eve

Peeking over the banister to see if Santa's coming

The anticipation I feel is ridiculous

What kind of man is this?

Is he heaven-sent or simply a figment of my imagination?

I'd say pinch me to make sure I'm not dreaming

But if I am – I'd rather you'd stab me so I could die in my sleep

For I wouldn't want to awake to a world without the man of my dreams

A sensation

Challenging every emotion I've ever felt regarding love

I feel pleasantly ill at the thought that I've finally found the definition of

My stomach is doing flips and I can feel my pulse beating in my finger tips

I feel the urge to scream and shout and at the same time I crave to cry

Releasing all my fears and disproving the lies

That love doesn't hurt and it definitely isn't blind

For the most pain he could possibly cause is when my stomach flutters; echoing the wings of butterflies

A sickening feeling and, ironically, a pleasant sensation at the same time.

Where should I begin?
Is my mind even capable of forming the words
I'd use to describe how you've stimulated me?
How you've single handedly
Without even touching me – frisked me?
Could I express how pleasantly violated I feel
From being searched by you?
Could my tongue even move in the proper way?
To utter syllables to tell you how elated I am that you have found me?
I wasn't hiding – you weren't looking
But we were there and were receptive
Open to the possibility
I – an empty vessel
Ready to hold all that you'd pour into me
Without leaking one single drop
I'd capture it all
Allowing myself to be hydrated, moistened and eventually softened
As I become clay
Submissively offering your hands the consent to personally mold me
Every inch, every crack and crevice formed as you please
Stamped with your signature for your pleasure
By your creative minds eye
I am pleased to say that I am yours
Am I capable of expressing?
That I am ready to be made by you?
Could I say it?
But where would I begin?

Daily I am wandering mentally
Fading to black like in a movie scene
Pulling back the curtains to envision my dreams
Emotionally I am lusting
Thirsting for those visions to become reality
Aching inside because I can't have what I see
Getting migraines from holding on so tightly to my fantasies
Carnality is winning and my flesh is weakening
I want it so bad that I find myself clenching my teeth
I can see it so clearly but it is so far from my reach
If I were close to the edge I would certainly fall over
Trying to grab what seems so real
It's more dramatic than a soap opera
But just the same – it's all a show
And when the curtains close
I am still all alone
As I open my eyes I dread the truth
My mind may be wandering but I am standing still
My emotions may be lusting
But they experience an orgasmic let down
Aroused by fabrications of what I wish had transpired
Enticed at the idea of experiencing my desires
Almost reaching the very climax of everything I crave
But the show is over
I'm back to practicality as I exit the stage.

I am discouraged
Because I can't read your mind
Impatient
Intimidated by my perception of time
Too proud to walk away and let it go
And too stubborn to listen when advised so
Curiosity is getting the best of my heart
Because images of you clutter my every thought
I have always been rebellious to societal order
I should allow you to lead and I should be dormant
But that's not me no matter how hard I try
I have to make my way to you as I push fear to the side
I envision grabbing you by the arm
Turning you around and offering my seductive charm
Hear me – hear me as I wear my heart on my sleeve
Love me, choose me, stay with me forever and never leave
See me – see me, you have to watch my every move
Read my lips – "love is a winning game and I will not loose"
Touch me – touch me and hold me close
Feel me – all of me from the flow my hair to the extension of
my pointed toes
Notice how soft I am and yet so firm
Those other chicks would never do – they have too much to
learn
I am the one – there is nowhere else to look
Put this ring on my finger, meet my folks and throw away your
little black book
You will never be uncertain – you will never have to read my
mind
I am every woman and I will cater to you until the end of time.

I admit it
I am anxious
I want it
I can damn near taste it

I've been broken
Though we have yet to touch
Pieces of me are everywhere
I physically confess

It's purely the flesh
Desire fills my veins
It keeps me living
I'm unable to deny its influence

Could I survive what happens next?
A whisper?
A glance?
The thought of a touch?

I doubt it!

Patient Love,

I can't wait any more

You and I both know we've been here before

We keep playing it safe but the anxiety I can't endure

I can see you in my dreams and feel you when you're gone

Patience is definitely a virtue and I'm trying to hold on

Eager to see what our love could be

Counting the days until I can give you all of me

Taking it slow at first so that we get it right

Hesitant to move too fast – contemplating spending the night

Don't want to be another statistic

Or just another notch on your belt

I'm so much more than a one night stand

I want to make certain that fulfillment is what's delivered and felt

I've been taunted in this manner before

And Anxious Love, he walked right out my door

This time around I've slowed it down

A lesson learned that's why you're still around

Still curiosity is getting the best of me

The patience I've learned is now thinning

You've kept my attention by waiting this long

Patient Love, thank you – now together let's greet the dawn

I offer vulnerability, trust and all that is mine

And readily our love will meet at the same time

I'm anticipating seeing what we'll become

If nothing at all, then back to lesson one.

I've never felt feels like this before

I can't recall the last time I ached inside, craving to explore

To learn of all that is unknown

To gain a better understanding of his abilities

As I admire his posture as he sits on his throne

From a distance I observe his movements

Tantalizing my inquisitiveness

He exudes excellence

Superior to any I've ever encountered or simply witnessed

I'm in awe of his confidence

His swagger is effortless

His presence demands attention and respect

It's as if God poured all that He could into this earthly vessel

There's nothing that he lacks

I selfishly consider him a gift for me

Thank you Lord, my eyes have seen your glory

I bask in his laughter and I blush at his smile

The climate even changes; his sweet breath ushers in a

soothing breeze for miles

More than a work of art

For nothing exists that could capture or explain his

magnificence

My weak attempt to depict his majesty serves no justification

To title him a "boss" would be an understatement

He is royalty; a King that will eternally reign

I've never felt feels like this before

I can't recall the last time I ached inside, but it's my pleasure to

endure.

Falling…
It's so easy to do
Just close your eyes
Let go and allow gravity to carry you
It could be perceived as courage
Or simply being carefree
Not considering the end result
Hopefully, I'll land on my feet.

Sensations

§

I just closed my eyes, outstretched my arms as wide as I possibly could, as my finger tips reached to the east and west, faced the north and exhaled. I'm feeling as relieved as a once panicked mother who thought she lost her child in a public place. I thought I was destined for solitude but he found me and hopefully he'll catch me. I just stood on my tippy toes, leaned forward and I am falling. Hell – I have fallen and it feels incredible. "To be loved…oh what a feeling" is right! It's a feeling of worth. This joy (pure high) has me under a spell that has made every moment of every day seem enchanted. No Disney story can compare to the ever-after ending I foresee. My life as Cinderella the stepsister is history and my future as his princess seems as certain as love at first sight. I believe that it exists and I have proof that there is such a thing as "chemistry".

The warmth of his touch and the soothing manner in which he strokes my hair, topped off with an *oh-so*-delicate kiss that he serves to the back of my neck and I'm officially under his influence. I deserve this. I deserve him and I deserve to be this happy. Victory is mine and loneliness has suffered an embarrassing defeat. In the midst of uncertainty regarding love, he has become my security blanket. This man is my place of refuge when I need shelter from the storm called "everything &

everybody". I've been waiting all of my life for this moment. I am in love.

I feel like Julia Roberts' character, Vivian, in the movie "Pretty Woman" – I have been RESCUED! I have been saved from the overbearing and tight grip that being alone has had on me. I appreciate him so much. I want to find a way to express how he's touched me in a special way. He has left his mark on my heart that will remain throughout time. I try to think of what I could do or what I could say to express how I feel but nothing seems to be good enough – nothing comes to mind. I thought of hugging him; yeah a warm embrace that will do. Then I realized my lips want to express their gratitude too. Okay so I'll kiss him as well, then I realized my heart has some things she wants to tell. So what can I do to honor every part of me and convey what a kiss and hug cannot accomplish alone? What could I offer that's so unique; something that I haven't already shown?

Wait a minute – ah hah, that's it! I'll offer my womanhood; the phenomenal and intimate characteristic that brands me a lady. There's a warm and incomparable place that rests in between my legs and yes I know that every female has one but they are not I – mine is exclusive, rare, and (if I can brag for a moment) *pure*. He hasn't experienced this before because mine has been tightly wrapped and packaged with *love*.

I can feel his breath

Rolling down the back of my neck

I can feel his fingers

Walking down my chest to my stomach

I can feel the throbbing

In sensitive places that leaves me wondering what's next

I can feel him

The welcoming warmth from his body

I feel the need as my flesh hungers

He presses up against me

I feel *e-v-e-r-y*-thing

My senses have never been so alert

Experiencing heaven

I think I just caught the Holy Ghost

I can smell the scent of him, every time the wind blows
A mixture of fresh and sweat tickles my nose

My body temperature increases while thoughts of him
stimulate my mind
Needing to be cooled, the wind arrives on time

I encounter a slight gratifying chill that erupts from the core of
Earth
Inviting his body heat to calm my nerves

Experiencing simple pleasures; priceless memories
Hopefully they will remain for eternity.

I imagine he's tasteful; as I lick my lips
Contemplating doing the same to his
Preferably the bottom – leaving it plump and swollen
His hands are rough and masculine
I benefit from them because they hold a tighter grip
Against my smooth skin, they'd have to slip on purpose
Falling onto and into places that provide them with moisture
As I naturally release fuel that ignites his upright posture
Ensuing simultaneous stimulation
I imagine he's tasteful; as I shiver while he's savoring
The moment – the desiring – yet we remain craving
Moistened and still thirsting – my mouth is watering.

So I leaned in to offer him a kiss
Closing my eyes; in an attempt to avoid the sight of possible rejection
Would he deny my flesh such a sweet and hesitant yet determined moment of carnal gratification?
Or would his lips too rise to the occasion?
My tongue quickly escapes, moistening my own in preparation
Blood begins to rush to a defenseless place unable to guard itself from involuntary awakening
Forcing me closer to this mass of a hopefully welcoming and pleasurable escape from reality
I land, cautiously – loosely
He remains firm and slowly offers pressure in return
Stealing my bottom portion with his teeth ever so gently
Receptive of the moment and diminishing my uncertainties
He pacifies my previously disturbed mentality
As I think to myself "yeah, he wanted me"
Feeling relieved of my insecurities and slightly overconfident
My body language extends an invitation, it reads:
If the remainder of you can move as expressively as your lips
Please dance all over me
I impatiently await your entire performance.

IN MY MIND…

I'm hearing the softest songs
As my body moves up and down
To the rhythm of his beating heart
A part of him dances just a *little* bit closer
To the source of my womanhood
Sneaking toward the core of me
That has yet to be stroked in such a manner as I anticipate
For a slight moment logic speaks to me
But it is quickly ignored
I've exposed myself
Encouraging him to prod as he so pleases
He recognizes the invitation
And pursues with domination
How did this erotic episode begin?
Within I feel unrestrained
Anxiety and curiosity are conquering my rational intellect
Allowing physical urges to be vulnerable
All of my senses are thoroughly aware
His sensitive touch
Awakens virgin sensations that I never knew rested within
This dance is an attempt to express
Sentiments I was unable to convey verbally
I give in faith of receiving
In hopes of forming a bond
Inspired by *love*
That can never be erased

My envisioned desire REALIZED…

My skin pressed against yours

Your forehead to mine

Perspiration drips from your skin

Landing on my spine

My symptoms are feverish

Between the fluctuating sweat and chills

At times a bit painful but worth it

So I carry on at my own will

Moaning and panting – inhaling and exhaling in unison

The heat in the atmosphere is becoming unbearable

Creating a natural combustion

Experiencing the fullness and spine tingling sensations

Yearning from the root of my soul

Collectively all of my emotions gather together

To form the most sensual, neurotic and uncontrollable
vibrations

That have my insides screaming

My spirit soaring and my heart racing

This experience is unimaginable

Unexplainable and definitely NOT to be understated

Engulfed in a blaze

Basking in my flaming heaven

I've got a feeling

That you won't be here in the morning

This evening has been incredible

I never imagined that every part of me could be edible

As the sun sets to reveal the moon's light

My flesh pleasingly marinates in your sweat

However my mind and emotions are entangled in a pessimistic web

I've got a feeling

That you won't be here to grin at the dawn with me

An expression that says, "ah yes, last night has left us restless"

Last night has left us voiceless and breathless, but it was worth it

As the pendulum of these potential outcomes swings in front of me

My body quivers, unexpectedly explodes and then quickly collapses

Time has passed, darkness arises, the night ends and I think perhaps....

You'll be here.

He captured me – and I loved it

I eagerly submitted

"Yes, please imprison me," my body screamed

Soothing all that ailed me

Pressure had never been so pleasing

My eyes were rolling and my body was quivering

In unfamiliar territory, I thought I was seizing – and I loved it

I wanted it – I needed it

I was willing to offer my life at that very moment

I pleaded to be abandoned in that trance

Seduction was not even necessary

I willingly surrendered as I threw up my hands

I dropped to my knees and I bowed my head

I couldn't speak a word if I wanted to

Between the gasps for air I could only manage to mumble

So I simply maintained my obedience

Compliant to his every command

He captured me – and I loved it

I'm begging, no…I'm demanding

Oh please detain me again.

Every time I close my eyes
I can still feel your skin pressed up against mine
I don't know what it is
Maybe because it's something new
But boy-oh-boy I bite my bottom lip when I think of you

Throughout the day
I'm still consistently trying to push thoughts of you away
But I can't
Mentally I am weak and I admit my flesh is too
Every time I inhale I breathe in the scent of you

I hold my breath so my high could be extended
Allowing fantasy to overtake me, my reality has ended
But I become too dizzy
And my legs get weak, so I exhale quickly
Searching for another method to feel you within me

As I open my eyes to realistic dismay
I bite my bottom lip again, craving for it to be you some day
But until then
I'll hold on to the memory of your scent
That natural high that keeps me lifted and my knees bent.

I'm envisioning the desire
The lust that once used to be
The flames that would immediately ignite
Because of the hazardous chemical reaction between you and
me

My skin pressed against yours
Your forehead to mine
Perspirations dripped from your chin
At times landing on my spine

You would moan, as I'd pant
Together inhaling and exhaling in unison
The heat in the atmosphere would be unbearable
Creating a natural combustion

Our symptoms were feverish
Between the fluctuating sweat and chills
At times it was a bit painful but worth it
So we'd pursue at our own will

Knowledgeable of the risk we'd take
The danger we'd put ourselves in
Living in the moment
And basking in our flaming heaven

I'm envisioning the desire
The passion that once used to be
I'm moist but no fire could ignite
For there's no chemical reaction if it's just me.

I gave in

I widened my limbs and offered my innocence

A sacrificial gesture to prove my sentiments and affection

I was so anxious to identify with its' ambiance

So ready to experience this physical phenomenon

To breathe heavily and to actually enjoy sweat

To feel the embrace and the sweet kisses of the opposite sex

I had to know; I was so tired of feeling deprived

I had to demonstrate my boldness, my independence and my
maturity

Yes, I too have a wild side

So I gave in

I bowed to the temptations that teased my flesh and haunted
my mind

Surrendering – since he gave his heart, he must deserve mine

Yes – I heard the warnings that my elders proclaimed

They wished they had waited – but they and I aren't the same

We are so different and living in different times

I am my own person and at this age I believe that I am wise

I will be careful, I am strong and I'll use protection

I submitted and now he's gone; I'm so lost

Waiting to regain his attention…

Harboring a feeling that leaves me a bit uneasy
As I look to the ceiling
I search for an answer that relieves me
Then I look into your eyes
Praying to find comfort there
I'm left disappointed – and even more scared
Afraid of yesterday, today and tomorrow
Bound by our circumstance
Leaving everything up to chance
Too intimidated by my own insecurities and sorrow
I would rather remain ignorant and quiet
And allow words to be left unsaid
I'd rather be hopeless with despair
It hurts much more to show that I care
Is this the outcome of yesterday?
That my silence continues today
And therefore we have no tomorrow?
Recollections of the past are all that will remain
Was it worth the investment?
Was there a valuable gain?

You've got me...
Going through these motions
Like a wave that rides the ocean
Out into the middle of nowhere
And the only thing I can relate to is the air
Simplicity is complex to me
All of my surroundings are fantasy
I'm so confused, I sometimes wonder if I'm being used
For your own pleasurable games
Otherwise, what else would I have to gain?
Except for those sleepless nights with thoughts of you
And those daydreams gazing at the sky so soft and blue
I am so unproductive with you on the brain;
Folks are whispering "she must be insane"
To be or not to be? Oh it doesn't matter
If you just lead the way I'll come running after
I am like a child; mold me, hold me, control me!
I'd willingly sell my soul if only to please thee

You've got me naseaus and going through!
You've got me in love with you!

DAMN IT!

It hurts – because the feelings aren't mutual.

I said a desperate prayer – pleading
That if this isn't the love for me
I'd no longer feel these emotions
That leaves me walking in a deep sleep
Barley existing through each day
My behavior has become mummified
Everything I do
From the movement in my walk as I sway
To how I wash in between my legs
Is an attempt to become your everything
As you are to me
I have a desire to love you
And just the same
I worship the idea that we never met
The aching to be loved by you
Increasingly becomes overwhelming
Now I wish those words you spoke were never said
"I was wondering if…"
And ever since I've been contemplative
Wondering if you are the love for me
Wondering if I will ever be your everything
Or am I still simply daydreaming?

It's a lonely night and the only comfort I can find

Is the thought of being loved by you

I'm sitting on the sofa waiting for your knock at the door

I can hear the words fall from your mouth, that you love me, you always have

You were being foolish and you were blind

But now you can see clearly and your heart is all mine

I begin to cry uncontrollably

As I fall to my knees and thank the Lord that you've come to your senses

You meet me there and promise to stay forever

You promise me more than the world; you'll attempt to give me heaven

I wrap my arms around your neck

The most precious and fulfilling embrace that life could offer

Overflowing with security and happiness that alleviates all of my worries

Finally! Finally we are a reality

You love me and you've admitted it

I always knew we were destined

I love you too; I only wish my imaginings would really happen.

Who said that it was love?
Not me
More like an infatuation or a fascination
Definitely not a love thing

Who said that it was love?
Was it you?
You can't even spell it; I'd let you tell it
But you never speak the truth

Who said that it was love?
Well they surely lied
Love is patient and kind; it doesn't envy or boast
And it damn sure wouldn't make me cry

It was oh-so-subtle how a trip on cloud nine became hazy and dull
Uninvited, a storm crept into our atmosphere
Washing away everything
I painstakingly watched her stream of filthy water
Visually interrogating her as she pushed our entire history into the sewer drains
Who is this bitch?
Where did she come from and how did she find me?
What aura did I emit to attract her misery?
How could you be so dumb to allow her to poison our purity?
She's arrogant…ignorant…uncouth…unattractive
Everything I am not; and you say that I am everything that you love
But still you tolerated her company?
Who is this bitch?
How did she know where we were vacationing?
I never knew a trip to cloud nine could end any way other than heavenly
I feel ashamed and embarrassed
The two of you have made me step out of my character
This unanticipated rainstorm has brought out the bitch in me.

I'll start by taking your number out of my phone
Though I know I have it memorized
At least my eyes won't have to see your name amongst my
contacts
Knowing damn well I once longed for your contact
Despite the obvious that you don't deserve to be in my
presence
I gave you ample opportunity, but you didn't know what to do
with me
I gave my all and catered to my man
But you took it for granted; all we had was an extended one-
night stand
Left with nothing but regrets in the palm of my hand
I tried my best to wash away the filth and the stench
But the scent of unwanted and neglect left me a wreck
Your ring tone used to give me butterflies
Now every time I hear that damn song on the radio I cry
So it's time to erase those seven digits, as hard as it is to do
It's the first step in my healing process; I HAVE to delete you
There was a time that I was tired of using technology and I
desired your touch
But now it has become sickening for me to even see your name
in my address book
The screen displays "Are you sure you want to delete?"
My fingers begin to twitch; will I regret this? Will he come
back to me?
Yes or no? Should I cancel or proceed?
I quickly recite your number aloud 2-6-7-L-O-V-E-M-E
But he never will and I'll never learn if I don't follow through
"Ughhhh" I grudgingly sigh aloud, "Goodbye, Baby. I'll miss
you!"

Have you ever tried to cry

But the wounds were so severe and intense

That when you closed your eyes

Even your tears were terrified to fly

For fear that any single movement would only deepen the pain

Hopelessness! Hopelessness!

I scream your name and I recognize your fame in my life

Emptiness, oh emptiness

I can feel your breath on my neck

I know you'll never leave

I admit I was a naive fool

I thought that I was rid of you

That I could go on and pretend you didn't exist

That I could push you over the edge

As I watch you fall to the bottom of my heart

That wide and useless hole – that empty abyss

Now I accept my fate

Married to eternal heartbreak

Hopelessness! Hopelessness!

I scream your name and I recognize your fame in my life

Emptiness, oh emptiness

I can feel your breath on my neck

I know you'll never leave

I've learned that happiness isn't for everyone

Definitely not for me

Sunny days are only in fairytales

And if I'm lucky, possibly in my dreams

Grudgingly I've come to grips with reality

I've accepted my depressing destiny – Hopelessness is me.

Silent tears I cry

No one can see them 'cause they fall on the inside

My heart is drenched with agony and pain

Inside my soul there's an eternal rain

I have to keep going and I can't let anyone in

They wouldn't want to be caught in this monsoon that falls within

Existing in this world – just trying to get by

With every step I stumble and with every breath I sigh

How could I be so alone in such a big place?

Everyone sees me happy, but I constantly wear a mask on my face

"Keep your head up," they say, "baby girl, don't give in"

How can I be encouraged when the turmoil never ends?

Wishing joy will come the next day; weary of being strong

Lord please save me from my masquerade – this show can't go on

I've been putting up a front for way too long

Somebody please hear the cries of my heart

Putting on a one woman show

I have to fake it through the hustle each day

I have so many roles

I am my own hero and villain in this play

Hear my words and please pray that I make it through

Love me or hate, I know you can relate

Lord I'm calling you now – tomorrow may be too late.

I've cried so many tears
I've bowed my head
So full of shame and fears
Regretful of my past
Things I could control
And others that were destined to happen
At times I would scream aloud
Asking "why?" and wishing for better times
I should've been on my knees
Instead my head was in the clouds
Giving up hope and wishing I could change my name
Born as someone else's child
Instead of into what I consider "the wild"
My life – that is – a fight to the finish
At times wishing the line was closer
I don't want to fight – the inspiration in me has died
The rage from disappointment has turned into a manipulated
expression
Recognized by most as smile
Masquerading through life – pretending I was free
Clandestinely enslaved within myself
The only one that I was fooling was me.

I'm crying tears from a broken heart
So many fears since our depart
Now a barbed wire fence blocks anyone from getting in
The thought of love makes me sick and tense
Will I ever attempt again

To give every single piece of me?
To invite every bit of him?
To vow that indefinitely our love will reign?
But I can't take the fame – the embarrassment
Everyone knowing – we've come to an end
I was so sure then

That today would never happen
You couldn't tell me
That I wasn't doing the right thing
Even if you yelled at me
I wouldn't have heard your warnings

Now reality sets in with fears of history repeating
That it will begin with late nights gazing at the stars
And end with me crying tears from a broken heart
As they fall from my chin and stain my chest
Hurt and disillusioned because I gave my best
Not wanting to know what happens next

The pain is unbearable; God forbid it doesn't get better
What I thought would last forever
Has left me writing a Dear John letter
Repeatedly playing sad love songs on the stereo
Constantly wishing I could change the entire scenario

I would have ended it and left him all alone
Instead of feeling like a rape victim
Despite the fact that I willingly gave in

But it's over now
I'm shadowed by a cloud so dark
Torrential rains pouring on me
Drowning out my tears from my broken heart.

I am mentally, physically and emotionally drained
The more I give, the more I can feel the blood being sapped
from my veins
After a while all that will be left of me is skin and bones
No heart, nor soul; I will eventually turn cold

There is only so much that a woman can give
Without being replenished; without being nourished so that she
too may live
I need food and water just the same as you
But you're so greedy that you inconsiderately consume mine
too

And all the while you're full and getting fat
I'm left with what you don't want; the crumbs – your scraps
I've come to a point where I've recognized my disease
The first step is acknowledgement – I am bulimic

I am tired of being this damn skinny to appease your appeal
I have to lose your dead weight so that I may begin to heal
Ironically, the first step to recovery is for me to diet
Once I cut down on you, I will be able to devour everything
else in sight…

And keep it!

You brought out the fool in me
In you I lost my dignity
Somewhere between the sheets
I dropped the essence of me
You see my grip wasn't tight to begin with
So your presence simply served as lubrication
To ease my hold so that I could easily lose control
I opened my legs, relinquished my power and innocence
As a consequence my soul escaped with instant regret and
heartache
To follow me the rest of my days
As I contemplate my mistakes
In my attempt to be giving and loving
I forgot about the "living"; the life in me
That's now lost as I die slowly
Afraid to breathe for fear it may be my last breath
I made a fool of me by allowing you to initiate my death.

I blame him
He did this to me
He broke me!
He broke US!
He took advantage of my thirst for love
My aching desire for companionship
It was set up right from the very beginning
With every smile in my direction he knew his intentions
weren't pure and were selfish HE HURT ME! HE HURT ME!
HE HURT ME!
He wasted my time – my precious time
I will never ever get those moments in life back again
Do you understand what I am saying?
What I am crying out?
He stole life from me!
It's killing me inside to accept our abrupt and ambiguous end
I can't even say for sure exactly when it ended or how it ended,
but it has ended
Did it ever really begin or was it just a figment of my
imagination?
Had I imagined everything?
Was he really not so wonderful?
Do I even know him?
Was he actually everything that I dreamed of or did I just
dream him up?
Was I that desperate?

In pursuit of him
My limbs became limp
My spine disintegrated
My mentality diluted with emotions
My heart hardened as a repercussion
My soul was caged, but unlike the bird, it had no song
My voice was silenced by the resounding of his wants
My desires were suppressed; terrified to fly
My independence surrendered at the fear of being lonely
My individuality conformed to his liking
My will was ignored as bondage grabbed a hold of me
My freedom was deprived so that I could have him by my side
In pursuit of him
I died.

Me…

Someone I am desperate to meet

She awaits me anxiously

For time keeps her from being revealed too early

There's something about her

I can just imagine her shadowing glow

Hovering over and embracing

Everyone she's destined to know

The energy she possesses

I have a feeling it is pleasantly overwhelming

Full of life and strength – a classic beauty

I live for the day that I hope to be

The most breathtaking moment I'll ever breathe

To meet her acquaintance & become in sync

To absorb her

All of her – until we are a unity

I wait anxiously

For life's lessons keep us estranged

Until we are destined to meet.

Melancholy

§

I've come to a critical point where I have drowned myself in so much despair, heartache, guilt and anger that it has become too heavy to bear and I truly believe that I have lost my mind from the chaos of it all. I constantly have headaches and I no longer walk upright because I am so slumped over with depression. It's nauseating. I actually feel as if I am committing mental suicide; with every ill thought it's as if I'm cutting my wrist. Each time I try to think of ways I could have prevented this pain; what should I have done differently? Where did I go wrong? It's as if I'm applying more pressure to the blade and penetrating my flesh. Of course it hurts like hell and yes, I absolutely do realize that if I continue it will only cause me further injury and possible damage that I may never be able to recover from. You'd think that I'd want to prevent myself from harm, especially if it could cause my own death, but I can't seem to stop myself. It's almost as if I'm having an out-of-body experience; I clearly recognize the pathetic self pity and though I'd rather live I am still cutting. I would yell out to someone but no one would hear me; after all it is all in my mind. I've become an emotional/mental cutter. Every day I awake it's as if the misery that has become me is realized all over again; I am *still* single and lonely – cutting deeper. I can actually feel the blood draining from my veins as life just pours out of me as if it were running from me – weakening me.

Why would life want to stay with me, this useless excuse for a woman? I'm struggling to catch my breath. I'm struggling to understand who I am, *why* I am and why I am not everything that I claim to be. Is the touch of a man really that important? Is sex that fulfilling that I had to completely indulge in it, constantly basking in the thought of it/him and abandoning me? Am I really that miserable by myself? These thoughts constantly and consistently torture me. I'm going crazy; even when I don't want to think about it they whisper to me, "You know you messed up right?"

The mind is powerful indeed and can be very overbearing and manipulative. If you're not strong enough and secure with who you are, what you want and where you're going, then you are doomed to a mentality of unfulfilling fantasies that will eventually bury your identity in imaginings. Ultimately the madness of it all steals life from you; gradually killing you. At this point I'm struggling to survive. Rather, I'm not even *struggling* at all because I'm not even attempting to live. I quit. I am so numb but somehow I can still feel the coldness that has overtaken me. As expected, death knocks at my door, and without hesitation or the common sense to turn him away, I open the door and usher him in. "Welcome," I say. He looks at me puzzled and replies, "What do you mean *welcome*? I've been here all along."

I hadn't noticed; I have become a zombie. I am theoretically dead. I am not trying to heal the self-inflicted wounds. I never once stopped to think, "you'll be ok – you can get over this." I'm not attempting to make any plans for my future. I am not trying to recuperate. At this point, I don't care to grow from or overcome this tragedy.

I am dead.

The concept that I still have life to live just doesn't sound feasible to me. I am spending so much time thinking about how he hurt me. Sometimes, I spend my days and nights contemplating ways to hurt him. I blame him; *he* killed me and it's time he pays his debt to society. That *murderer*!

I am totally ignoring the obvious; it was *I* who gave in. It was *I* who allowed him to become my everything. *I* gave so much and expected little in return, aside from his companionship. I *longed* for flesh – for the warmth of his body lying next to me as if it were the answers to all of my lifelong prayers. I devoted my time, attention, thoughts, energy, wardrobe, culinary skills, understanding, compassion, lust, forgiveness, tears, kisses, hips, thighs and everything in between. I devoted *my life* to him. The truth is too big of a pill to swallow. The worst part of it all – the part that makes me gag and choke and actually wish that I actually did die from suffocation (and not a quick and painless death, because I do deserve to suffer) – is the fact that he never asked for it. I just gave it to him.

Considering my definition of love I thought that if I gave it then I would receive it in return. Stupidly, I was so preoccupied with loving him that I forgot about loving *ME*. I pushed all of my desires to the side and – dare I say it, can I say it? My tongue aches at the thought of uttering these two words – *I SETTLED*! I settled? Yes, I settled. I settled for companionship and completely overlooked commitment. Rather, I settled for moments of bliss manipulated by thoughts of lust and the carnal satisfaction of flesh. Put plainly – the sex was good. I settled for sex! With every stroke and penetration inside of me he temporarily hushed my concerns about being alone and lonely. The comforting way his body cradled mine somehow reassured me that my journey through life would not go un-witnessed. His straight lined and tender kisses from my forehead to my toes were all the evidence I needed that he loved me. God *knows* I miss those kisses! Actually I miss those moments of ignorance when I really believed that everything was perfect. Now I painfully grasp how imperfect and poisoned my mentality had become. It hurts even more to acknowledge that his sex was just pacifying my flesh and the whole time my heart was still crying out, "what about me?"

I forgot about my heart.

I forgot about me.

Would I even recognize my own reflection? What happened to the powerful woman that I *claimed* to be? Had the beast in me died? I am woman; hear me purr? As these thoughts are ruffling through my mind I can't help but to feel like an abused pet; afraid to move and terrified to make a sound. Maybe if I just sit here quietly under my cloud of shame no one will notice the storm of stupidity that constantly falls on me.

Ughhhh, but it's so lonely here, so in an attempt to occupy my time I keep on cutting. The voices in my head continue as they whisper thoughts about what my life would've been like had I not fallen from the throne of womanhood. How would I be perceived by the man that *is* for me (the one individual that I actually do want to notice me)?; would he even want me knowing that I wasn't pure and free, now that I am officially branded "crazy"? I realize that I am now just some tainted, scorned and neurotic piece of lonesome flesh who walks around under an isolated storm cloud of idiocy, mumbling to herself, "you dumb bitch," and shouting to others, "watch out now!...I'm single...don't mess with me!" Life itself is running from me so why would any man come near me? What's my worth? Would somebody *please* just institutionalize and medicate me!

Meanwhile, the voices continue...

You've fallen – *I'm crazy*

Laying flat on your face – *and talking to myself*

With mud in your eyes – *pretending I can still see*

Though your vision is blinded – *I choose to play "make believe"*

You're filled with disgrace – *but only if I stay in reality*

Embarrassed and ashamed – *but shhhh, they can't see me*

You know you made a mistake – *I am Queen of Misery*

While living for your flesh – *My filthy flesh, Hannibal Lector wouldn't even eat me*

You've gained heartache – *Here, you can have my heart; it betrayed me*

Could you ever forgive yourself? – *Could I ever forgive me?*

Will you ever forget? – *Will I ever forget?*

You're doomed to misery! – *Duh, I am Queen of Misery*

With a life of regrets! – *Yes! Regrets are my friends*

How could you be so dumb? – *Duh, because I'm crazy*

Now you feel so numb – *That's the best way to be*

There was no love, just lust – *Freak me baby, awww yeah*

You can't take this pain – *Well then I'll ignore it*

You should just ignore it and sleep – *That's what I just said!*

You're on the verge of going insane – *No silly, I've already fallen off the cliff*

Your most precious gift you did not keep – *Now we agree!*

These overwhelming emotions have captured my soul and taken me hostage.

They gagged and kidnapped me in the calm of the night.

I awoke in an unfamiliar place realizing I can't beat them no matter how hard I fight.

There's a war going on and I'm a casualty.

I'm outnumbered and unequipped – no one has ever told me I'd experience captivity such as this.

It's a struggle but I must escape. I won't allow them to know my weaknesses nor my secrets.

I must stay strong; I cannot break.

Who the hell do they think they are to invade my territory and subdue me?

I swore that I was prepared for battle; thought I'd mastered the art of war.

Damn it – I'm the commanding general in this army!

They can yell at me, beat me; they can torture me if they must, but I vow to never give in.

I'll ride this thing to the death. I can't be a valuable hostage if I'm no longer living.

Anguish rests inside like a pulsating cyst

Can I close my eyes and wish it away, pretending that it doesn't exist?

What would tomorrow be like if I kept quiet and resisted temptation?

Would life be better if I suppressed my devastation?

Put a smile on my face and laughed despite the heartache?

Embraced the company of others though I prefer to push them away?

I'd be content to sit in an airless room

No noise, no light – just me and my thoughts are allowed in my earthly tomb

Others say I have to keep breathing

This too shall pass I'll see, yet my lungs are ready to burst

All of my organs have been coerced

They've been persuaded by my heart to gang up on me

I swear I can feel them marching

In preparation of battle and determined to be victorious

Who knew self-inflicted pain could be so notorious?

Will they break me? Should I wave my white flag recklessly?

I surrender, knowing damn well that they're going to kill me

What other choice could I make?

My options are death or living with continuous heartache

I choose to die for living is overbearingly agonizing

Let it be over; the reality of everyday life would only patronize me.

This is my world
Shades of grey overcast everything
My face remains expressionless
My pulse struggles to catch the beat
I've fallen
Fallen way too deep in my own misery
Insecurity and disgrace arrested me
No bail was set
And the only judge that could free me
Has gone on recess
This is my world
Deserted – I'm stranded
Confined to a place with endless destinations
Surrounded by fears and oblivious to the realization
That I could go anywhere
For this is my world
It is I who choose to remain here
In desolation and isolation – ignorant
So quick to yell "I want more"
I need more
So slow to move – I refuse to open the door
Opportunities are waiting in foreign un-traveled land
But this is my world
Right here where I stand.

Tapping my fingers rapidly

Patting my foot in sync

Staring off into space

Thought of the day: "can I escape?"

Am I forever trapped?

A prisoner of my own restraints?

Have I learned my lesson or did I just skim through the pages?

I've never been so nervous

There are so many choices

It seems easier to stay here

Could I remain stubborn?

Would I be content?

Do I have the strength to let go?

To move on?

To attempt to live?

I've never been so scared

The uncertainty is breaking my heart

Am I being too animated, emotional and sensitive?

Is this really minimal compared to what I have yet to experience?

Is it worth it, this suffering?

Did I lose my way?

Will I ever find me?

Will I ever leave this place?

Or should I accept my permanent residency?

I became neurotic

My mind constantly occupied with fears of being mistreated

Couldn't see past the concrete evidence of my past that bruised me

An unseen force was hindering me from living

Determined to bury me right there in wretchedness

I became desperate for every and anything

Something or someone to rescue me from me

I waited grudgingly

So long until I noticeably wore my own anguish

My hat tilted ever so arrogantly

To match that tightly wrapped scarf around my neck that held in my insecurities

The same material as the gloves of hindrance to prevent my ability to feel

So that I could remain numb, and to prevent vulnerability

My coat did so well in bundling me to wrap me within myself

Protecting me from the cold of reality and the winds of trust

Somehow I forgot about the damage that could be accomplished from sweat

I held so much inside until it began to pour down the back of my neck

Eventually drenching me in my not-so-preventative attire

Saturating my anxieties as they all poured out

Causing me to emit steam; becoming more uncomfortable within my own skin

From out of nowhere a voice within me screamed

"Undress me from this misery! I'd rather live in the nude than die from overheating!"

Then another voice whispered....

Trust me
I know you better than you know yourself
All that I have for you is more than you could ever imagine
If you would only trust me I can fulfill every crack, crevice and
void
Through me you will be complete
I love you! You are My daughter, My heart, My love
I created you because I saw a need in the world
My answer to this deficiency is the gift I've instilled in you
Only you, because I uniquely designed you comparable to no
one else
My heart jumps when you speak to Me
I get so excited when you come to Me for advice
But the best way to make Me proud is to give Me what I gave
you
Your life
Trust Me
It is only a minimal sacrifice
Because all that I have for you exceeds a lifetime
There is no love that any man could offer you
That you don't already possess within
Because it is My love that I placed there
A love that heals, a love that strengthens
A love that endures, a love that's eternal
A love that's pure, a love that's all Mine
And now it is all yours
Trust Me
I know you better than you know yourself
Because you are My Love.

There's something in the air
Intangible yet forceful

Ushering in reality
Commanding me to behave cautiously

The true colors of he who was my everything
Are not those of roses as I believed

As I reluctantly remove the tinted film from my mind
My perception of truth and reality becomes

As distinctive as black is from white
There's something in the air

As clear as water
Yet it is so visible

The winds begin to bluster severely
Loosening the foundation of "*him*" that I knew

I'm frozen with fear at the idea
Of him being shades of imagination

And not variations of flawlessness
As I had imagined – as I needed him to be

The winds grow faster and stronger
A necessary hurricane is forming

Transforming pessimisms into rational realisms
He is but a blemished man who never cared for me

A heart wrenching blow to endure
The result of which has left my world disheveled and feeling
insecure

As I look around at the leveled and wrecked remainings
I realize the storm of truth wasn't that fierce

I'm a little shaken up
But I am *still* standing.

Conscious

§

I thought I understood the concept of love. I was certain that I knew what it meant to be a woman. I really believed that in addition to being strong and nurturing, I was supposed to be submissive to my man. I was so certain that my love for him would evoke his love for me and it would be the kryptonite to keep me going. Instead it broke me down. I began to feel used and useless and I became lust itself. Continuously yearning to be loved but, in its place, settling for the physical expression. The first man that came along and gave me some attention, I gave my heart, then my mind and eventually my body. My entire being – my soul itself – was held hostage. I was restrained by the possibility of what he could be to me; therefore my life conformed to his. I didn't recognize my self-worth. I did not realize that any man worth my time (moments of my life that I will never relive) would be willing to wait for me. I never would have fathomed that mutually consented sex could cause so much anguish. It's frustrating. All I can think about is the time I've wasted; the life that I've lost spent in the captivity of ignorance – and it hurts. All I do is cry all the time now. I'm in tears as I write this very sentence, tonight on December 2, 2008 at 11:31 p.m. But why?

I'm crying because I'm afraid. I don't even feel like crying. I'm sick and tired of tasting my own salty tears. Yet, I'm crying. I'm crying because I recognize that I have to let go and actually believe in something more than what is in front of my eyes. There has to be more to life than this pain. If I'm not hopeful then I'll just die. I'm crying because this realization only means that there is a lot more uncertainty to come. I've learned that the definition of faith is to believe, despite the lack of physical evidence, that God will give me the desires of my heart. I trust Him, right? So why am I crying? I'm crying because I'm thinking of the suffering I'll endure from delayed gratification. I'm crying because I realized that I tried to use sex as a manipulating tool to keep a man. I'm crying because I grasp that sex isn't a tool that measures love. I'm crying because I once encouraged women on the topics of love and relationships but now (considering my history of heartache, mistakes and ignorance) I'm not sure that I have anything optimistic to say. I'm crying at the thought of coming home alone and not having anyone to hold me at night. I'm crying because I'm terrified at the thought of a man losing interest in me because I'm not having sex with him, and therefore I'm feeling pressured to do so.

I'm still crying. I'm crying at the thought of the inevitable – that I will *have* to be alone in order to heal. I'm crying because I don't believe that I am strong enough. I will really go insane if I have to come home to an empty house *e-v-e-r-y day*. It will be torture to lie in my bed, probably going through my mental rolodex of past moments, and then becoming even more aggravated because I miss the touch of a man. I can imagine the agitation while thinking "Why can't I just give in?" But then those voices whisper "it's because you don't know how to separate emotions from the physical act of sex". I'm not even sure if I'm capable. I just don't believe I was created to handle it. I don't just have sex with anybody so how could I think that I'd be able to disconnect the two?

I'm crying because all I really want is for someone to love me for me. I'm crying because I don't even know *me* because I've spent so much time catering to and trying to impress others. I'm crying because it hurts even more now to realize how much growth is necessary before I can be in a relationship, which means a longer period of time *alone*. I'm crying because all of these damn thoughts are stampeding through my mind and I feel as if I'm never going to survive this catastrophe. It's only getting worse. The voices in my head are becoming terrifyingly exasperating. I'm at the edge of the cliff and I'm ready to freaking jump!

TO HELL WITH THIS INSANITY!

I can't take it anymore! I don't want to bear this burden any longer. I hate these thoughts. These overpowering emotions of anger, frustration, sadness, guilt, self-pity and hopelessness are going to be the death of me and I'm ready to surrender. I can't stop crying. My chest hurts. I can't breathe. I'm not even making a sound but my body is reacting as if I'm screaming. My lungs are fluctuating rapidly and the tears are just pouring. My head hurts like hell. My heart is going to explode – *Aaaaaaaaaaah*!!!

There it is – there's the sound! **Aaaaaaaaaaaaaaaaaaaaaah!**

God, it feels good to just scream – just to let it all out and let it go. I don't want it anymore! Yes, GOD! (As if I just remembered He exists). *Please* take it? Please help me!

God, I need YOU because I can't do this by myself!

I know You know what's best for me. I know it! I've always known it! I thought I could do it on my own; I really believed I could, but I've endured too many unnecessary scars along the way and I don't know how to heal them myself. *Pleeeease*, God. Please save me from myself. Please have mercy on me and show me your grace and your love. Please *love me*, flaws and all; I know You're capable. I'm on my knees in the middle of what seems to be a freaking nervous – mental – emotional – spiritual – physical break down and I'm surrendering. I surrender. I surrender *ALL*!

Tears began overflowing
And then I heard You call my name
Whispering softly to me that everything is about to change
I could feel the strong winds blowing at the eye of the storm
Heartache pulling me in every direction
Disfiguring my original form
Everything I'd known no longer felt the same
Peace was gone, days seemed extremely long
Life as I knew it had changed

Cry to me, my child
I heard His voice so clear
Let it all out until there is none left to release
Every pressure and every burden with every single tear
Come to me my love and I will give you rest
Let me wrap my arms around you
Your soul my Holy Spirit will caress

In the midst of tragedy, feeling lonely and weak
I am weary, I am desperate and it is Your face I seek
Save me from this chaotic world
Save me from myself
I'm running towards You with all of my might
And I'm bypassing everyone else
There's only You I see ahead of me
Lord, You are my strength
I know Your love will carry me
No matter what I'm up against.

Farewell burden
I don't want you anymore
I choose to live
If I stay I'll die for sure

Complacency never looked good on me
To choose you
I'd be settling
I crave to live
To meet life itself

What better gift, could God have given?
A chance to breathe
An opportunity to cry all inspired tears
To suffer sorrow

To value bliss
To enjoy a single moment
The excitement of anger
The serenity of affection

The vagueness of tomorrow
The assurance in Him
I crave to live
To meet God Himself

I crave to live – only to live
For me, there is nothing else
Give me life
Give me so much more

Until I take my last breathe
Give me all that I could possibly yearn for
To live every single moment
And to feel with every part of me

To experience all
And to be absent from nothing
To encounter death
Only once I've had it all

So I won't desire to live another moment
So I could have a chance
To say
I've lived.

Awakening

§

That's it, isn't it? This is what I've been missing. This very moment is what God has been waiting for; my submission to *His* will and not that of my own or that of a man. I was so constrained by my depressive thoughts and my circumstances that I didn't even realize that the "Him" I should have been focusing on still loved me. God still loved me! GOD, the single most complete and accurate expression of "love", *still* loved me despite me. The One who created me, chose me, allowed me to live; the One who has been there with me since my trip through the birth canal and promised to never leave me – *that* One. The only One who could restore me to my rightful and royal throne of Womanhood, I had been ignoring. Now that I stand at death's door, more desperate than ever, I finally acknowledge Him. But why now? The voices start again: "Was it necessary for me to come to the terminal stage of my breakdown in order for me to break through? Am I that hardheaded? Am I that naïve? Am I that ignorant?" NO!!! I won't let them win this time. They cannot have the best of me. They will not kill me. They will not incapacitate me of my birthright to experience life abundantly. At this point of my desperation I don't even care as to "why". I thought I was anxious for companionship but that is nothing compared to my recently rediscovered will to live! I will live, I decide! As I bow my head and close my eyes in an attempt to see more clearly:

Dear God,

*I don't know why You love me. I cannot
understand Your mercy but I am grateful that it
endures my ignorance. I recognize my faults
and Your grace that kept me despite my
behavior. I come to You from the position that
my insanity has brought me to – on my knees. I
am overflowing with humility and in reverence
of Your power, asking for forgiveness. I truly
believed that my intentions were pure – to love
and be loved – but I realize now that I forgot
about loving You. I forgot about Your love for
me. I ignored Your will for my life; a life in
which every aspect of it has been designed by
You, especially the honor to be a woman. I was
so caught up in the hardships of womanhood
that I didn't recognize the blessings. Yes, we do
have a demanding and vital role to play, but we
are Your daughters.*

*I am the child of a King; a princess born into
royalty, continuously seeking my crown in
preparation of being someone's divinely
appointed Queen. I know now that I did not
behave as Your princess should. I displayed
peasant-like behavior and received a peasant-
minded man in return. A man who was only out
for his needs and feeding off of the weakness of
others so that he could survive. I cannot blame*

him for what I allowed him to do to me. If I did
not display royal mannerisms how could he
have known that he should have treated me as
such? I so willingly offered him all that You
gave me without asking You if it was his to have.
I admit that I put myself in that situation and I
ask for Your compassion: I ask that my mistakes
not be held against me; that I may learn from
them and heal from the wounds that they have
left. I am drained and I desperately seek
restoration. As I fall asleep tonight I pray that I
find Your love to greet me in the morning.

Now I lay me down to sleep
I pray the Lord my soul to keep
I pray the Lord to instill in me the gift of discretion
The ability to recognize what is and what is not a blessing
I ask of this because as You have witnessed
I have exercised poor judgment
I have made decisions that weren't in my best interest
Seeking my own desires
And now I am experiencing the repercussions
I should have put my trust in You; instead I offered it to man
And here I am down on my knees asking You to mend the
wounds
So that I may never relive this insanity again.

And when I awoke, my King was *still* there.

I slowly opened my crusted eyes
Attempting to rid my fears
As I un-balled my clenched fist
I began to release the tension I held on to so dear

I could feel everything
As oxygen pushed the blood through my veins
Throat a bit sore but I'm breathing
I'm alive again and I remember my name

I was lost in him – in sin
Drowned so deep til' death
No matter how hard I fought
I just could not seem to catch my breath

Then a word was spoken to me
Something rooted since birth
Live your life and live abundantly
You only have one visit to Earth

I began to cry
Warm and wet tears – just streaming
Releasing the hurt and mending the wounds
Then I smiled – I realized I'm healing.

It's morning; everything is so fresh, so new
Another chance to try again
Another chance to win

Thinking of last night and everything I said
It even hurts just to recall
To think I almost lost it all

The darkness of the night quickly fell
I forgot about the sweetness of the day
I stumbled; I fell and almost lost my way

I went to sleep in my self-created misery
But said a prayer before I closed my eyes
And while I dreamt God used that time to remind:

Tomorrow will bring the morning
Everything will be so fresh, so new
Awake and believe in the blessings that I have given you

It's morning; thank God it's morning
I can remember the sweetness of the day
It's morning; it is only morning
And just think, I still have the rest of the day.

How does it feel to be free?
To feel the breeze of peace
And the raindrops of liberation
As the sun's rays offer light onto those once dark places
To embrace security with every step
As your toes caress Earth's dirt
The assurance of a sturdy foundation
As opposed to attempting to walk on water and feeling
uncertain

What does it mean to be free?
To recognize the uncertainty of tomorrow
And still call it beautiful
Accepting that He directs your path
Therefore you don't have to be fearful
As you acknowledge the present and enjoy its liberty
Surrounded by endless destinations
And knowing that right here where you stand – you are free.

Her Peace of Mind
§

A few years ago Lauryn Hill performed on MTV and she sang a song titled "I Gotta Find Peace of Mind". She sat on a stool, hugging a guitar in her arms and she sang the song with every bit of her being. The performance brought her to tears; beautiful, flowing soft tears that effortlessly fell. She performed for her audience, but even more so the moment became worship unto the Lord. I admired her vulnerability but I couldn't understand her emotions – until now. I can hear her in my mind as she sings "I know it's possible to finally be in love and know the real meaning of a lasting relationship..." I am sitting here at this very moment and I am in tears; beautiful, flowing soft tears that effortlessly fall. I'm crying tears of joy, tears of *peace*; because I know that *it is* possible.

It is possible to be free. It is possible to be in love. It is possible to be at peace. It is possible to have a lasting relationship. It is possible because I believe. I believe in me. I believe in love. I believe in God and His love that has never left me. He has a perfect plan for my life that is beyond my comprehension and the fact that He brought me this far (overcoming so much despair) is a testament of just that. He could have left me right there crying my eyes out in the middle of the night – aching for love, aching for morning to come – but He didn't. He LOVED me enough to wrap His arms around me right there in that moment and save me before self-destruction occurred. He loved me enough to rescue me from myself and to free my mind.

I've heard the phrase "Whatever a man thinketh so is he." I understand this to mean whatever you allow to occupy your thoughts (whether it is fears, lust, a career choice, love, etc.) will eventually manifest because your actions will follow your thoughts as instructed by your brain. My emotional breakdown and mental destruction had largely to do with the fact that my thoughts were constantly focused on man. I conjured up ideas about who he was, who I wanted him to be, what I wanted from him and who he could potentially have been in my life. I placed him on a mental pedestal that should have been occupied with meditations of God and His purpose for me. Instead there was a vacancy that I filled with fantasies that eventually distorted reality. My thoughts began to materialize because I actively and ignorantly pursued them. I made up in my mind that I knew what was best for me and I went for it, only to realize that I didn't even know myself as well as I thought I did. I didn't understand that I was created by God (the ultimate expression of love itself) and only God knew what was best for me.

He is my Knight in Shining Armor. He saved this damsel in distress. He touched me and instantly warmth consumed my earthly flesh and I knew He was the one. And, now that I possess this knowledge and confidence I can patiently rest assured that He will appoint me someone to experience life with.

I acknowledge that the waiting period may not be the easiest task. However based upon life experiences and lessons, I've learned that only time can reveal true blessings and true blessings will come to those who are patient. In the Bible, the book of John 1:4 says:

> *"But let patience have her perfect work, that ye*
> *may be perfect and entire, wanting nothing."*

I love this verse for several reasons; firstly that patience is recognized as a "her." It gives me the belief that women were designed to endure the long run. The definition of patient is "bearing pains or trials calmly or without complaint."[1] And, in order to master the lifelong lesson of being patient I have to expect that there are going to be situations that arise that will test my patience. In order to develop strength I have to be conditioned just as weak, flimsy muscles must be built up by gradually increasing the amount of weight they can endure. A person who has never exercised in their life cannot expect to lift one hundred pound weights and not tire (if they can even lift it at all.) But with patience, endurance and determination, *in time* they can expect to be able to complete several reps of lifting those one hundred pounds and even more. Therefore, I know that I am going to be confronted with situations when I feel inferior and/or weak, but my strength comes from the Lord, my King, who can take the weight of the world off of my shoulders. For a moment I thought, "well, if I need to be made stronger then shouldn't I carry the load myself?" But then I realized that sometimes being strong means knowing when to let go and surrender.

---

[1] http://www.merriam-webster.com/dictionary/patient

Secondly, I am in awe of this verse because it states *"ye may be perfect and entire, wanting nothing."* Through patience and the conditioning process of becoming the woman God designed me to be I am made whole and will want for nothing. It does not say "let patience have her perfect work, then you'll find your husband, and then ye may be perfect." This means that I don't have to seek a man to make me complete. I am whole within myself. God provides for me so that I will want for nothing. He will provide for His daughter, His princess, who seeks His will for her life; to become a virtuous woman.

Another scripture that is dear to my heart and compliments what I've just said is Proverbs 31:10-12:

> *"Who can find a virtuous woman? For her price is far above rubies. The heart of her husband doth safely trust in her, so that he shall have no need of spoil. She will do him good and not evil all the days of her life."*

This assures me that God does intend for me to be blessed with a husband and that He does not intend for me to be single forever. However, I recognize that the particular type of woman that a man of God should be seeking is one of virtue. It is not my job to seek after my man as I originally believed. It is my obligation to bear the trials of single life *calmly, without complaint and in a virtuous manner*. Ultimately, what I want is for my husband to love the God that he sees in me, to recognize me as the daughter of the King and to value me as such. I understand this now. In the meantime, I am to live life to the fullest. I humbly accept my rightful place on the throne of Womanhood throughout my journey, to become the Queen that God created me to be, and I embrace it joyfully.

I acknowledge that I only have one opportunity at life – *just one* – and while I'm here I want *everything* that God has to offer me when He decides that I am ready to have it. Yes, one of those blessings is a husband to love and cherish me, but I am not going to lose any more precious time sulking because I don't yet know him or have him in my life. My plan is to actively pursue God's love so that I may continue to love myself as a Queen should. And when the tornado of anxiety, fear and loneliness swirls around me in an attempt to corrupt my mind I won't run around frantic like a chicken with its head cut off in an effort to avoid its effects. I will not seek after a man as if he's this powerful force field that will protect me from the harsh elements. No! I will remain still, calm and assured that my strength comes from the Lord. My sanity will remain as secure and as firm as my rock – my God – and in Him I sustain my peace of mind.

So to you, who are reading this at this very moment, I invite you to close your eyes so that you can see clearly; your King is just a prayer away and He's waiting to escort you down the aisle to crown you a sane and virtuous woman. Join me; it's very liberating where I am. One night with my King literally changed everything. It's an unimaginable experience to embrace the love of the One who first loved you; to know that He will be there in the morning, to stand tall and confident and know that you are His own. It is amazingly revitalizing to realize that your existence is evidence that you are exactly what you've been searching for...*love itself*. Remember, it is possible.

Remember that you are not alone. You are not the only woman to feel what you are feeling. We *all* have experienced life's harsh lessons of understanding love but praise God because we are capable of learning those lessons and preventing future unnecessary heartache. Remember God instilled in us that desire for companionship and to love. The key is to understand that "*falling in love*" is a hopeful, child-like, gullible joy that can hold reality captive, but to *learn to love* is to capture reality. The reality of it all is this, what God has for you is far beyond what you could ever ask or think; peace that surpasses all understanding.

> "And the peace of God, which transcends all understanding,
> will guard your hearts and your minds in Christ Jesus."
> ~Phillipians 4:7

Dear Queen,

Live your life with your soul open to feel the
breezes of the wind.
Your mind closed to the formalities of this world
that restrain your desire to live for Him.
Walking with confidence down roads that
haven't been traveled by any other being.
Taking the challenge head on with faith; without
fear and without seeing. Trusting His Holy
Spirit that navigates every step of your course,
to sustain your sanity and avoid remorse.
Please live virtuously and abundantly while
patiently awaiting your earthly king.

Love,
Liz

"Just because God is still preparing your King, doesn't mean
that you're not already a Queen."

~Bishop T.D. Jakes

She stands tall, so full of beauty and grace
Her head tilted to the side with her eyes opened wide
She has a self-assured look on her face
Her posture is impeccable
And in her eyes there is a gleam
They alone testify that she has witnessed things
That one would've never imagined she has seen
She recalls all of the obstacles that have been presented by life
She barely smiles, still a dimple appears
She chuckles as she shakes her head and gently closes her eyes
She has experienced heartache, physical pain and neglect
Not to mention the loss of self-love at one time, something she
never expected
Through it all she can still crack a smile and feel secure
She knows that life is what it is – an obstacle course
There are times that she has to jump high
And moments when she must lay low
There have been struggles that required her to crawl through
the mud
Through it all she projects an undeniable glow
Her state of mind is tranquil with an optimistic attitude
Determined never to give up or give in
Encouraged by her own ambitions
She is a secure woman!

I am free –
I'm fluttering past all I have ever known
Shedding the past while still embracing my history
An undeniable testament that I have grown

Learning to love me and all that I encompass
Doing so as I continue to love you
And not allow it to cause me any distress

I'm accepting the faithful changes in life
And as they force my emotions to surface
They won't overtake me nor encourage strife

Thinking logically without diminishing my sensitivity
My mind and my heart work together
Along with my soul, the three are an indestructible trinity

I am fluttering, I am flying – I am escaping
I was ignorantly caged within myself
Now that I have wings there's no restraining me – I am free!

Little girl, little girl —what do you know?

I know I'm precious and beautiful
And in me there is a seed that God has sewn

Little girl, little girl – what do you see?

I see unlimited blessings more than my mind can imagine
My heart can't even fathom what God has for me

Little girl, little girl – what do you feel?

I feel peaceful, secure and boundless
A heart once broken now has been healed

Little girl, little girl – what have you learned?

I've learned to whom much is given much is required
He gave me life, but heaven has yet to be earned

Little girl, little girl – my how much you have grown

Why thank you; I am a woman now
A Queen that will never be dethroned.

I don't want to and I can't imagine where I would be
If it weren't for the blood that poured from His side for me
A crown of thorns stabbing Him in His head
Splinters in His back from the wood that became His bed
Welts and bruises – abrasions on His skin
As He cried out "Father why hast thou forsaken me?"
All for me
I couldn't carry that burden and I wouldn't want that cross to
bear
Yet He stood in my place so that I could stand here
And remind us all of the definition of love
And where we would be if it were not for His blood.
And with this said please don't let another moment go by
And not acknowledge the Lord and savior of our lives
The very next moment could be your very last
And the last thing I would want my God to ask
Is "my child why hast thou forsaken me?"
When I sent my son to set you free
He told us to live our lives and live abundantly
He gave us His word – literally
He gave us a second chance, again and again and again
But only because of the blood that washed away our sins
Nothing but the blood…nothing but the blood of Jesus.

There is something about praising You
That eases all of the pain
Releasing suffering, with only joy to gain

There is something about loving You
That uplifts my spirit
The warmth when I mention Your name feels just as good as
when I hear it

There is something about trusting You
That relieves my fears
The security in knowing Your word is sincere

There is something about believing in You
That makes the hard times seem minimized
Compared to the gifts from You that I can't even fathom in my
mind

There is something about acknowledging You
As I go throughout my day
Just a prayer of thanks that I have made it and I am sane

There is something about praising You
That eases all of the pain
Uplifts my spirit
Relieves my fears
And makes the hard times seem minimized
As I go throughout my day

There is something about the name of Jesus.

Tears inspired by Him are only for the purpose of growth, release or joy
With the intentions of bettering you, for your happiness is His joy
You never have to wonder where He's been or if He's being honest with you
He's always there when called and your existence is evidence that His word is true
He's only concerned with your future; He forgives and forgets past indiscretions
His desire is for you to become royalty as you experience life's lessons
His love for you is unconditional and He's anxious to give it to you
He offers you all of His attention; whenever, wherever, whatever – His intentions are pure
He cares for you because of who you are and what He's instilled in you
He wants to be with you forever because He is just that into you.

I am radiant
Displaying the pureness of light that is me
Romantically in love with myself
In a way that God fashioned me to be

My heart now smiles so brightly
Filled with God-given inner peace
The glow that my presence projects
Can only be described as a natural luminosity

I traveled the corners of my soul
In search of self-serenity
All the while I should have remained still
And allowed my divinely ordered steps to lead me

I felt my way through the darkness
With His spirit steering me
Saved just as dusk turned to dawn
My joy surely came in the morning.

Eternal Peace

§

I can only pray that His will for you will conquer your own
That humility will become you and you'll never again travel
this road alone
I can only hope that your life will be long-lived and that sorrow
won't outweigh bliss
That you endure less painful tears and more tears of laughter
followed by a sweet kiss
I can only imagine the beautiful and precious experiences that,
I plead with destiny, await you
The ones that you dream of every night but are disappointingly
snatched back by the daylight
Those dreams that make you want to dream longer and never
see a new day
The aspirations that have your imagination running wild and
your soul longing to be carried away
I pray that your existence won't go un-witnessed; that your
legacy will start as a whisper and grow so loud that it must be
written
In the beginning there was His word alone that formed all of
life; the most important, an heir to His throne who – for you
and me – made the ultimate sacrifice
And in the end, when the trumpet sounds, only His word will
remain.
I can only pray that written in His word will be your life, your
soul, your legacy – your name.